Contents

The Little Book of
Nursery
Rhymes

www.alligatorbooks.co.uk

The Alligator logo is a registered trade mark of
Alligator Books Ltd.

The Little Book of

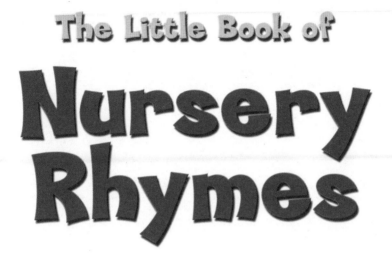

Nursery Rhymes

© 2016 Alligator Publishing Ltd

Published by
ALLIGATOR PUBLISHING LIMITED
2nd Floor, 314 Regents Park Road,
London N3 2JX

Printed in China 0433

Humpty-Dumpty

Humpty-Dumpty sat on a wall,
Humpty-Dumpty had a great fall,
All the King's horses and all the King's men,
Couldn't put Humpty together again.

If Wishes Were Horses

If wishes were horses,
Poor men would ride.
If turnips were watches,
One would be by my side.
And if 'ifs' and 'ands'
Were made of cheese,
There'd be no work for
busy bees.

There Was a Crooked Man

There was a crooked man, and
he walked a crooked mile,
He found a crooked sixpence
against a crooked stile.
He bought a crooked cat, which
caught a crooked mouse,
And they all lived together in
a little crooked house.

Pease Porridge Hot

Pease porridge hot,
Pease porridge cold,
Pease porridge in the pot,
Nine days old;
Some like it hot,
Some like it cold,
Some like it in the pot,
Nine days old.

Lucy Locket

Lucy Locket lost her pocket,
Kitty Fisher found it;
Kitty saw nothing in it,
But the binding 'round it.

Little Miss Muffet

Little Miss Muffet,
Sat on a tuffet,
Eating her curds and whey.
Along came a spider,
And sat down beside her,
And frightened Miss Muffet away.

Cock-a-Doodle-Doo

Cock-a-doodle-doo!
My dame has lost her shoe,
My master's lost his fiddle stick,
And they don't know what to do.

Cock-a-doodle-doo!
What is my dame to do?
Until my master finds his stick,
She'll dance without her shoe.

Cock-a-doodle-doo!
My dame has found her shoe,
And master's found his stick,
Sing doodle-doodle-doo!

Cock-a-doodle-doo!
My dame will dance with you,
While my master fiddles
  with his stick,
For dame and doodle-doo.

Baa Baa Black Sheep

Baa, baa, black sheep,
Have you any wool?
Yes sir, yes sir,
Three bags full.
One for my master,
One for my dame,
And one for the little boy
Who lives down the lane.

Georgy Porgy

Georgy Porgy, pudding
  and pie,
Kissed the girls and made
  them cry.
When the boys came out
  to play,
Georgy Porgy ran away.

Peter Piper

Peter Piper picked a peck
of pickled peppers.
A peck of pickled peppers
Peter Piper picked.
If Peter Piper picked a peck
of pickled peppers,
Where's the peck of
pickled peppers that
Peter Piper picked?

Hush-a-Bye

Hush-a-bye baby,
On the tree top,
When the wind blows,
The cradle will rock;
When the bough breaks,
The cradle will fall,
And down will come baby,
Cradle and all.

13

Wynken, Blinken and Nod

Wynken, Blinken and Nod one night,
Sailed off in a wooden shoe,
Sailed off on a river of crystal light,
Into a sea of dew.
"Where are you going, and what do you wish?"
The old moon asked the three.
"We have come to fish for the herring fish,
That live in the beautiful sea.
Nets of silver and gold have we!"
Said Wynken, Blinken and Nod.

The old moon laughed and sang a song,
As they rocked in the wooden shoe.
And the wind that carried them all night long,
Ruffled the waves of dew.
The little stars were the herring fish,
That lived in the beautiful sea.
"Now cast your nets wherever you wish,
Never afraid are we."
So cried the stars to the fisherman three:
Wynken, Blinken and Nod.

All night long their nets they threw,
To the stars in the twinkling foam.
Then down from the skies came the wooden shoe,
Bringing the fisherman home.
It was all so pretty a sail it seemed,
As if it could not be.
And some folks thought it was all a dream,
Of sailing that beautiful sea.
But I shall name you the fishermen three:
Wynken, Blinken and Nod.

Wynken and Blinken are two little eyes,
And Nod is a little head.
And the wooden shoe that sailed the skies,
Is the wee one's comfortable bed.
So shut your eyes while Mother sings,
Of wonderful sights that be.
And you shall see the beautiful things,
As you rock in the misty sea,
Where the old shoe rocked the fishermen three:
Wynken, Blinken and Nod.

17

Thirty Days Have September

Thirty days have September,
April, June and November;
All the rest have thirty-one,
Excepting February alone,
And that has twenty-eight
days clear,
But, twenty-nine in each
leap year.

Three Blind Mice

Three blind mice!
See how they run!
They all ran after the
    farmer's wife,
Who cut off their tails with
    the carving knife!
Did you ever see such a
    thing in your life?
Three blind mice!

Mistress Mary, Quite Contrary

Mistress Mary, quite contrary,
How does your garden grow?
With silver bells and cockleshells,
And pretty maids all in a row.

Little Bo-Peep

Little Bo-peep has lost her sheep,
And doesn't know where to find them.
Leave them alone and they'll come home,
Bringing their tails behind them.

Little Bo-peep fell fast asleep,
And dreamed she heard them bleating.
But, when she awoke, she found it was a joke,
For they were still a-fleeting.

20

Then up she took her little crook,
Determined now to find them.
She found them indeed, and then she did plead,
For they'd left their tails behind them.

This Little Piggy

This little piggy went to market,
This little piggy stayed home,
This little piggy had roast beef,
This little piggy had none.
And this little piggy went,
"Wee, wee, wee" all the way home.

There Was an Old Woman Who Lived In a Shoe

There was an old woman who lived in a shoe,
She had so many children, she didn't know what to do.
She gave them some broth without any bread,
Then she scolded them loudly, and put them to bed.

Girls and Boys Come Out To Play

Girls and boys come out to play,
The moon is shining as
  bright as day.
Leave your supper,
  and leave your beds,
It's time to awake,
  you sleepy heads.
Come with a whoop,
  come with a call,
Come with good cheer
  or come not at all.
Up the ladder and down
  the wall,
A halfpenny roll will
  serve us all.
You find milk,
  and I'll find flour,
And we'll have pudding,
  in half an hour.

Little Jack Horner

Little Jack Horner,
Sat in a corner,
Eating his Christmas pie.
He put in his thumb,
And pulled out a plum,
And said, "What a good
    boy am I!"

Little Boys and Little Girls

What are little boys made of?
Snips and snails and puppy dogs' tails,
That's what little boys are made of!

What are little girls made of?
Sugar and spice and everything nice,
That's what little girls are made of!

Jack and Jill

Jack and Jill went up the hill,
To fetch a pail of water.
Jack fell down, and broke his crown,
And Jill came tumbling after.

27

The Queen of Hearts

The Queen of Hearts, she made some tarts,
All on a summer's day.
The Knave of Hearts,
He stole the tarts,
And took them all away.

The King of Hearts, called for the tarts,
For the Knave had broken the law.
The Knave of Hearts brought back the tarts,
And promised to steal no more.

Hey, Diddle, Diddle

Hey diddle, diddle!
The cat and the fiddle,
The cow jumped over
  the moon.
The little dog laughed
To see such a sport,
And the dish ran away
  with the spoon.

Sing a Song of Sixpence

Sing a song of sixpence,
A pocket full of rye;
Four and twenty blackbirds,
Baked in a pie.
When the pie was opened,
The birds began to sing;
Was it not a pretty dish,
To set before the king?
The king was in his treasury,
Counting out his money.
The queen was in the parlour,
Eating bread and honey.
The maid was in the garden,
Hanging out the clothes.
Along came a blackbird,
And pecked off her nose.

The Hobby-Horse

I had a little hobby-horse,
Its coat was dapple grey.
Its head was made of straw,
And its tail was made of hay.
I sold it to a grandma,
For some dimes and nickels.
With the money I received,
I bought a jar of sour pickles.

Pat-a-Cake

Pat-a-cake, pat-a-cake,
Baker's man,
Bake me a cake,
As fast as you can;
Prick it and pat it,
And mark it with T,
And put it in the oven
For Teddy and me.

Wee Willie Winkie

Wee Willie Winkie runs
through the town,
Upstairs and downstairs
in his nightgown,
Rapping at the window,
Crying through the lock,
"Are the children in
their beds, it's now
eight o'clock?"

Jack Sprat

Jack Sprat could
eat no fat,
His wife could eat
no lean;
And so between
the pair,
They licked the
platter clean.

Hickory, Dickory, Dock

Hickory, dickory, dock,
The mouse ran up the clock,
The clock struck one,
The mouse ran down,
Hickory, dickory, dock.

Polly, Put the Kettle On

Polly, put the kettle on,
Polly, put the kettle on,
Polly, put the kettle on,
   And let's have tea.

Yankee Doodle

Yankee Doodle came to town,
Riding on a pony;
He stuck a feather in his cap,
And called it macaroni.

Mary Had a Little Lamb

Mary had a little lamb,
Its fleece as white as snow,
And everywhere that
  Mary went,
The lamb was sure to go.

Early To Bed, Early To Rise

The rooster crows in
the morn,
To tell us to rise,
And he that lies late,
Will never be wise:
For early to bed,
And early to rise,
Is the way to be healthy
and wealthy and wise.

Here We Go Round the Mulberry Bush

Here we go round the
mulberry bush,
The mulberry bush, the
mulberry bush;
Here we go round the
mulberry bush,
On a cold and frosty
morning!

Oh Where, Oh Where Has My Little Pup Gone?

Oh where, oh where has
my little pup gone?
Oh where, oh where
can he be?
With his ears cut short
and his tail cut long,
Oh where, oh where
is he?

38

Hush Little Baby

Hush little baby, don't say a word,
Mama's going to buy you a mockingbird.
And if that mockingbird won't sing,
Mama's going to buy you a diamond ring.
And if that diamond ring turns brass,
Mama's going to buy you a looking-glass.
And if that looking-glass gets broke,
Mama's going to buy you a billy goat.

Monday's Child

Monday's child is fair of face,
Tuesday's child is full of grace,
Wednesday's child is full of woe,
Thursday's child has far to go,
Friday's child is loving and giving,
Saturday's child works hard for
   her living;
But the child who is born on
   the Sabbath day,
Is merry and lucky, and good
   and gay.

The Clock

There's a cheerful little clock,
In the schoolhouse it stands,
It points to the time,
With two little hands.
May we all be like the clock,
Cheerful and bright,
With our hands ever ready,
To do what is right.

40

Ding, Dong, Bell

Ding, dong, bell,
Pussy's in the well!
Who put her in?
Little Johnny Flynn.
Who pulled her out?
Little Tommy Stout.
What a naughty boy
  was that,
Try to drown poor pussycat,
Who ne'er did any harm,
But killed all the mice in
  the Farmer's barn!

41

Old Mother Hubbard

Old Mother Hubbard,
Went to the cupboard,
To get her poor dog a bone;
But when she got there,
The cupboard was bare,
And so the poor doggy
  had none.

She went to the butcher,
To buy him some meat;
But when she came back,
The dog would not eat.

She went to the doctor
To ask him to help;
But when she came back,
The doggy was well.

She took a clean dish,
To give him a drink;
But when she came back,
He was under the sink.

She went to the hatter,
To buy him a hat;
But when she came back,
He was feeding the cat.

She went to the barber,
To buy him a wig;
But when she came back,
He was dancing a jig.

She went to the fruiterer
To buy him some fruit;
But when she came back,
He was playing the flute.

She went to the tailor
To buy him a coat;
But when she came back,
He was riding a goat.

She went to the cobbler,
To buy him some shoes;
But when she came back,
He was reading the news.

She went to the seamstress,
To buy him some linen;
But when she came back,
The doggy was spinning.

She went to the market,
To buy him some bones;
But when she came back,
He was playing with stones.

The dame made a curtsey,
The dog made a bow;
The dame said, "Your servant,"
The dog said, "Bow-wow."

45

Old King Cole

Old King Cole,
Was a merry old soul,
And a merry old soul was he;
He called for his pipe,
And he called for his bowl,
And he called for his
   fiddlers three.
Each fiddler had a fiddle,
And a very fine fiddle had he;
Twee-tweedle-dee,
   tweedle-dee, went the
   fiddlers,
Oh, there are none so rare,
Who can compare,
With old King Cole and his
   fiddlers three!

Peter, Peter, Pumpkin-Eater

Peter, Peter,
  pumpkin-eater,
Had a wife and
  couldn't keep her.
He put her in a
  pumpkin shell,
And there he kept
  her very well.

To Market, To Market

To market, to market,
  to buy a plump pig,
Home again, home again,
  dancing a jig;
To market, to market,
  to buy a fat hog,
Home again, home again,
  jiggety-jog;
To market, to market,
  to buy a sweet bun,
Home again, home again,
  the day is now done.

One, Two, Buckle My Shoe

One, two,
Buckle my shoe;
Three, four,
Shut the door;
Five, six,
Pick up sticks;
Seven, eight,
Put them straight;
Nine, ten,
A good fat hen;
Eleven, twelve,
Ring the bell;
Thirteen, fourteen,
Maids a-courting;
Fifteen, sixteen,
Maids a-wishing;
Seventeen, eighteen,
Maids a-painting;
Nineteen, twenty,
My stomach's empty.

Pussy-Cat, Pussy-Cat

Pussy-cat, pussy-cat, where have you been?
"I went to London to visit the queen."
Pussy-cat, pussy-cat, what did you there?
"I frightened a little mouse under the chair."

Little Robin Redbreast

Little Robin Redbreast,
Sat upon a rail;
Niddle, naddle, went his head,
Wiggle, waggle, went his tail.

Banbury Cross

Ride a cock-horse to
Banbury Cross,
To see an old lady on
a white horse;
Rings on her fingers and
bells on her toes,
And so she makes music
wherever she goes.

Hot-Cross Buns

Hot-cross buns,
Hot-cross buns,
One a penny, two a penny,
Hot-cross buns!
Hot-cross buns,
Hot-cross buns,
If you have no daughters,
Give them to your sons!

53

I Saw a Ship a-Sailing

I saw a ship a-sailing,
A-sailing on the sea;
And oh, the ship was loaded,
With pretty things for thee!
There were sweets in the cabin,
And apples in the hold;
The sails were made of silk,
And the masts were made of gold.
The four and twenty sailors,
That stood between the decks,
Were four and twenty white mice,
Gold chains around their necks.
The captain was a duck,
With a parcel on his back;
And when the ship began to move,
The captain said, "Quack, Quack!"

Cobbler, Cobbler, Mend My Shoe

Cobbler, cobbler, mend my shoe!
Give it a stitch and that will do.
Here's a nail, and there's a blade.
And now my shoe is well made!

Little Boy Blue

Little Boy Blue, come blow
   your horn.
The sheep's in the meadow,
   the cow's in the corn.
Where is the boy that cares
   for the sheep?
"He's under the haystack,
   fast asleep."
Will you wake him? "No,
   not I;
For if I do, he's sure to cry."

Simple Simon

Simple Simon met a pie man,
Going to the fair.
Said Simple Simon to the pie man,
"Let me take a pair."
Said the pie man to Simple Simon,
"Show me first your penny."
Said Simple Simon to the pie man,
"Indeed, I have not any."

Ring a Ring O' Roses

Ring a ring o' roses,
A pocket full of posies,
Ashes, ashes,
We all fall down!

Rain

Rain, rain, go away,
Come again another day,
Johnny and Jemma want
to play.

Roses Are Red

Roses are red,
Violets are blue;
Daisies are sweet,
And so are you!

Twinkle, Twinkle

Twinkle, twinkle, little star,
How I wonder what you are?
Up above the world so high,
Like a diamond in the sky.

Rub-a-Dub-Dub

Rub-a-dub-dub,
Three men in a tub,
And how do you think
  they got there?
The butcher, the baker,
The candlestick-maker,
They all jumped out of
  a rotten potato,
It was enough to make
  a man stare.

Bedtime

The man in the moon
  looked into the room,
Looked into the room and said,
"It's time for all children
  around the world,
To hop into their cozy bed!"